The C**O**LOR Bear

Written by Barbara Brenner
Illustrated by Bob Ostrum

McGraw Hill **Wright Group**

Copyright © 1996 by Wright Group/McGraw-Hill.

Printed in the United States of America.

Send all inquiries to:
Wright Group/McGraw-Hill
P.O. Box 812960
Chicago, IL 60681

ISBN 0-02-686684-6

 6 7 8 9 SCG 10 09 08 07 06 05 04

The McGraw·Hill Companies

The bear was sitting
On the grass,
Eating honey
From a glass.

The bear was **brown.**

The grass was **green**.

The honey was **yellow**.

And the sky was **blue.**

Here's the way it was:
The brown bear sat
On the green, green grass,
Eating the yellow honey
From a glass.
And the sky was blue.

Then along came a
Little cloud of **gray**.
The bear said, "I think that
It may snow today."
He put on his **purple** hat.

A cold, wet wind
Began to blow.
The bear said, "It certainly
Looks like a giant snow."
He put on his big, **red** boots.

The snow began.
It fell thick and white.
The bear said, "I think that
It might snow all night."
He put on his **orange** mittens.

So the **brown** bear sat
On the **green, green** grass,
Eating the **yellow** honey
From a glass,

Wearing a **purple** hat
And big **red** boots
And **orange** mittens.
And the sky was **blue**.

It snowed for **one** hour.
The grass got white.

It snowed for **two** hours.
The boots got white.

It snowed for **three** hours.
The mittens got white.

Four hours. The honey
And the glass were white.

It snowed all night and . . .

Everything turned white.

The white bear sat
On the white, white grass,
Eating white honey
From a glass.
White hat on his head.
White mittens on his front paws.
White boots on his back paws.

The sun came
To melt the snow.
First a bit of **blue**
Began to show.

Then **yellow.**

Then a little **purple**.

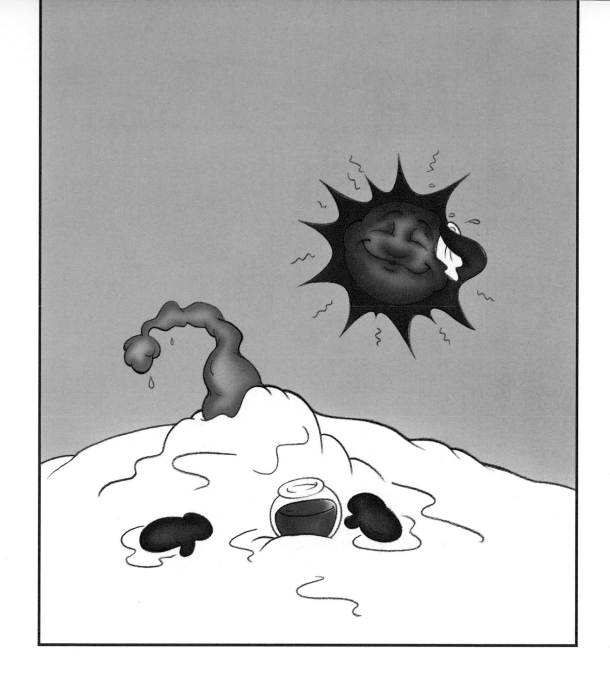

Then some **orange**.

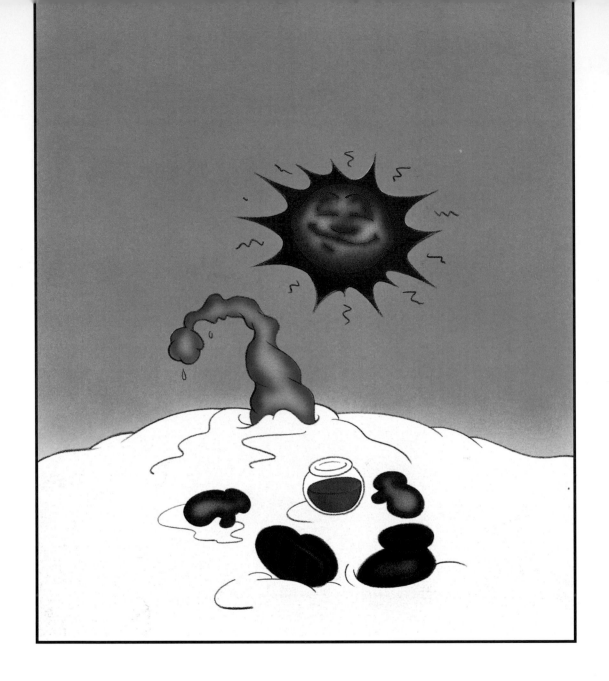

Next a little **red.**

And then **green**.

But where
Was the **brown** bear?

The brown bear had sneaked away
To sleep until
Some warm spring day—
The way bears do.

And as he slept,
He dreamed ...
A dream of colors.